P9-BZR-561

CONSUMER MATHEMATICS 2
FRACTIONS, DECIMALS,
AND PERCENT

CONTENTS

Author:	**Barbara L. Hintze**
Editor-In-Chief:	Richard W. Wheeler, M.A.Ed.
Editor:	Robin Hintze Kreutzberg, M.B.A.
Consulting Editor:	Robert L. Zenor, M.A., M.S.
Illustrator:	Thomas Rush

AOP

804 N. 2nd Ave. E., Rock Rapids, IA 51246-1759
© MCMLXXIX by Alpha Omega Publications, Inc.   All rights reserved.
LIFEPAC is a registered trademark of Alpha Omega Publications, Inc.

FRACTIONS, DECIMALS, AND PERCENT

If we limited ourselves to whole numbers, much mathematical activity would be impossible. Any arithmetic or rational number that is not a whole number is a fraction of some kind. Fractions are essential to proper manipulation of much of the data available to us. For these reasons, and others, we embark upon a study of fractions.

OBJECTIVES

Read these objectives. The objectives tell you what you will be able to do when you have successfully completed this LIFEPAC.®

When you have finished this LIFEPAC, you should be able

1. To define a fraction.

2. To define the numerator and denominator of a fraction.

3. To identify and work with proper and improper fractions and mixed numbers.

4. To add, subtract, multiply, and divide fractions.

5. To use fractions in problems involving measurement, purchasing, distribution, and other consumer activities.

6. To convert fractions to decimals.

7. To convert decimals to fractions.

8. To add, subtract, multiply, and divide numbers involving decimals.

9. To solve consumer-related problems using decimals.

10. To change decimals and fractions to percent.

11. To change percents to decimals and fractions.

12. To work base-rate-percentage problems.

13. To solve consumer-related problems with percents.

Survey the LIFEPAC. Ask yourself some questions about this study. Write your questions here.

_____

_____

_____

_____

_____

_____

_____

_____

_____

I. FRACTIONS

OBJECTIVES

1. To define a fraction.

2. To define the numerator and denominator of a fraction.

3. To identify and work with proper and improper fractions and mixed numbers.

4. To add, subtract, multiply and divide fractions.

5. To use fractions in problems involving measurement, purchasing, distribution, and other consumer activities.

You have no doubt met fractions before. If you are like most people, you found the meeting at least mildly unpleasant. Most people stay away from fractions as much as they can. However, fractions are more or less inevitable. We need to know how to deal with fractions when we find them.

One of the reasons fractions are inevitable is that things in this world rarely come out even. You may have ten cookies and three people to distribute them to. Hardly ever does your mother buy a whole pie or cake per person. Activities don't usually last exactly an hour. The tank of gasoline needs more than five gallons, but less than six. The dress takes three yards of material and a little bit more. These pieces, these leftovers, these divisions are fractions. If an arithmetic number is not a whole number (remember them?) it is a fraction.

Another reason that fractions are inevitable is that so many of them exist. In fact, for every whole number, an infinite number of fractions exists. For example, take the whole number 3. Some of the fractions involving 3 are $\frac{3}{2}$, $\frac{3}{3}$, $\frac{3}{4}$, $\frac{3}{5}$, $\frac{3}{6}$, and so on. Since so many fractions are around, we are bound to run into them sooner or later, so let's get on with learning how to deal with them.

TERMINOLOGY

What is a fraction? You may know what a fraction looks like, but a formal definition of what a fraction is should help you to understand and use fractions.

DEFINITIONS

A. A *fraction* is a symbol consisting of three parts: a horizontal bar, a whole number above the bar, and a whole number other than zero below the bar.

B. The *numerator* of a fraction is the number above the bar.

C. The *denominator* of a fraction is the number below the bar.

Models: A. $\frac{2}{5}$, $\frac{7}{16}$, $\frac{8}{3}$, $\frac{0}{7}$, $\frac{13}{13}$

B.   The numerator of $\frac{7}{13}$ is 7.

C.   The denominator of $\frac{7}{13}$ is 13.

A fraction can represent several different situations. Sometimes it represents a *part of a whole*. When I say that I have $\frac{5}{8}$ of a pie left, I mean that the pie was cut into eight pieces and three of them are gone.

Sometimes a fraction represents a *division*. The fraction $\frac{5}{8}$ can mean 5 divided by 8.

Sometimes a fraction represents a *ratio*. If I say the class is $\frac{5}{8}$ girls, I mean that the ratio of girls to people in the class is 5 to 8. That is, for every eight people in the class, five are girls.

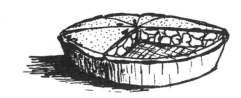

When you read a fraction, you usually say a *th* after the name of the denominator. For example, $\frac{3}{8}$ is read *three-eighths*; $\frac{4}{11}$ is read *four-elevenths*. This method is correct, but can get awkward when the denominator is large. We usually use the word *over* for fractions with large denominators. For example, $\frac{3}{107}$ is usually read *three over one hundred seven*.

████████ Write definitions for the following words.

1.1 fraction _____

_____

1.2 numerator _____

_____

1.3 denominator _____

_____

████████ On the blanks, write three items a fraction can represent.

1.4 _____

1.5 _____

1.6 _____

If the denominator of a fraction is larger than the numerator, then the fraction is less than 1. For example, $\frac{5}{8}$ and $\frac{4}{7}$ are less than 1. (Remember that one meaning of $\frac{5}{8}$ is that we had eight pieces, and three are gone). This type of fraction is called a *proper fraction*.

┌───┐
│ DEFINITION   │
│   │
│ **Fractions** that are less than 1 are called *proper fractions*. │
└───┘

If the denominator of a fraction is smaller than the numerator, then the fraction is greater than 1. For example, $\frac{16}{7}$ is greater than 1. (Remember that one thing a fraction can represent is a division. 16 divided by 7 is more than 1). This type of fraction is called an *improper fraction*.

4

An improper fraction can be written as a
mixed number. The improper fraction $\frac{16}{7}$ can be
written as $2\frac{2}{7}$. Notice that $2\frac{2}{7}$ has a whole
number part (2) and a fraction part ($\frac{2}{7}$).

DEFINITIONS

An *improper fraction* is a fraction that is greater than 1.

A *mixed number* contains a whole number part and a fraction part.

Suppose the numerator and the denominator
of a fraction are equal. What kind of fraction
do we have? This kind of fraction is just
another way to write 1. For example, $\frac{3}{3}$, $\frac{13}{13}$,
$\frac{97}{97}$, $\frac{1,046}{1,046}$ are all ways to write 1.

On the blanks identify the fractions as *proper*, *improper*, or
mixed. If the fraction is a way to write 1, put 1 in the blank.

1.7 $\frac{3}{8}$ _____   1.10 $\frac{17}{18}$ _____

1.8 $4\frac{3}{4}$ _____   1.11 $\frac{18}{17}$ _____

1.9 $\frac{16}{12}$ _____   1.12 $\frac{17}{17}$ _____

Another definition related to fractions
describes *equivalent fractions*.

DEFINITION

Equivalent fractions are fractions that have the same numerical value.

Model 1:   We saw that $\frac{3}{3}$, $\frac{13}{13}$, and $\frac{1,046}{1,046}$
           all have the same value: They
           are all equal to 1. Therefore,
           they are equivalent fractions.

Model 2:   Notice that $\frac{3}{6}$ is equivalent to $\frac{1}{2}$.

Model 3:   Notice that $\frac{1}{3}$ is equivalent to $\frac{4}{12}$.

We find fractions equivalent to any given
fraction by multiplying or dividing the numerator and the denominator of the fraction by
the same number.

Model 4: $\frac{15}{20}$ $\frac{15}{20} = \frac{5 \cdot 3}{5 \cdot 4} = \frac{5}{5} \cdot \frac{3}{4} = 1 \cdot \frac{3}{4} = \frac{3}{4}$

           If we divide 15 by 5, we
           get 3. If we divide 20
           by 5, we get 4. Therefore,
           $\frac{3}{4}$ is equivalent to $\frac{15}{20}$.

Model 5: $\frac{3}{8}$ If we multiply 3 by 60, we get 180. If we multiply 8 by 60, we get 480. Therefore, $\frac{180}{480}$ is equivalent to $\frac{3}{8}$.

Each fraction has many equivalents.

Find two fractions equivalent to each given fraction and write them in the blanks.

1.13 $\frac{1}{3}$ a. _____   b. _____

1.14 $\frac{21}{28}$ a. _____   b. _____

1.15 $\frac{3}{5}$ a. _____   b. _____

1.16 $\frac{100}{200}$ a. _____   b. _____

1.17 $\frac{7}{12}$ a. _____   b. _____

1.18 $\frac{6}{9}$ a. _____   b. _____

If the numerator and the denominator of a fraction can both be divided evenly by a certain number, we call this number a *common factor*. If the numerator and denominator have a common factor, the fraction can be reduced by dividing both numerator and denominator by the common factor. For example, $\frac{9}{12}$ can be reduced to $\frac{3}{4}$ by dividing both numerator and denominator by 3. Note that the new fraction is equivalent to the original. When the only common factor is 1, the fraction is said to be *reduced to lowest terms*.

DEFINITIONS

A *common factor* is a number that divides evenly into both the numerator and the denominator of a fraction.

A fraction is *reduced to lowest terms* when the only common factor of the numerator and the denominator of the fraction is 1.

Reduce the following fractions to lowest terms. Some may already be in lowest terms. If so, write them in the blank as they are.

1.19 $\frac{7}{14}$ _____   1.21 $\frac{3}{8}$ _____

1.20 $\frac{6}{9}$ _____   1.22 $\frac{20}{25}$ _____

Since fractions are arithmetic numbers, we need to learn how to perform arithmetic operations with them. First, let's
talk about how to add and subtract. Multiplication and division come next.

ADDITION

If the fractions we want to add (or
subtract) have the same denominator, what
we do is add (or subtract) the numerators
and put the result over the denominator.

Models: $\quad \dfrac{3}{11} + \dfrac{6}{11} = \dfrac{3+6}{11} = \dfrac{9}{11}$

$$\dfrac{1}{3} + \dfrac{1}{3} = \dfrac{1+1}{3} = \dfrac{2}{3}$$

$$\dfrac{7}{12} + \dfrac{7}{12} = \dfrac{7+7}{12} = \dfrac{14}{12}$$

$$\dfrac{6}{9} - \dfrac{2}{9} = \dfrac{6-2}{9} = \dfrac{4}{9}$$

Add or subtract the following fractions and write the answer on
the line.

1.23 $\quad \dfrac{1}{4} + \dfrac{2}{4} =$ _____

1.24 $\quad \dfrac{3}{8} - \dfrac{2}{8} =$ _____

1.25 $\quad \dfrac{6}{11} + \dfrac{3}{11} =$ _____

1.26 $\quad \dfrac{4}{10} - \dfrac{3}{10} =$ _____

1.27 $\quad \dfrac{8}{9} - \dfrac{3}{9} =$ _____

1.28 $\quad \dfrac{7}{7} + \dfrac{3}{7} =$ _____

1.29 $\quad \dfrac{14}{3} + \dfrac{6}{3} =$ _____

1.30 $\quad \dfrac{6}{13} - \dfrac{1}{13} =$ _____

Suppose, however, that we want to add two
fractions that do not have equal denominators.
For example, suppose we want to add $\frac{3}{4}$ and $\frac{2}{5}$.
We need to change these fractions in some way
so that we can add them. What we do is change
them so that they have the same denominator,
and then we can add them as we did before.
Now, the question is, how do we change $\frac{3}{4}$ and $\frac{2}{5}$
so that they have the same denominator?
Remember how to find a fraction equivalent
to $\frac{3}{4}$? We can find an equivalent fraction
by multiplying both numerator and denominator
by the same number. Suppose we use 5. We
find that $\frac{15}{20}$ is equivalent to $\frac{3}{4}$, the first
fraction we want to add. Now consider $\frac{2}{5}$,
the second fraction we want to add. If we
multiply both numerator and denominator by 4,
we find that $\frac{8}{20}$ is equivalent to $\frac{2}{5}$. Now we
can add $\frac{15}{20}$ and $\frac{8}{20}$ and get $\frac{23}{20}$.

How do we determine what to multiply by to make the denominators the same? We find a *common denominator*.

DEFINITION

A *common denominator* of two fractions is a number that both denominators will divide into evenly, with no remainder.

In our example with $\frac{3}{4}$ and $\frac{2}{5}$, we find a number that both 4 and 5 will divide into evenly. That number, 20, becomes the denominator of our answer. Then we find the equivalent form of each fraction that has that number for a denominator.

Let's look at another example. Try to add $\frac{3}{7}$ and $\frac{1}{4}$. What number will both 7 and 4 divide into evenly? Right, 28. So 28 becomes the denominator of our answer. How do we find an equivalent of $\frac{3}{7}$ that has 28 for a denominator? We multiply both numerator and denominator by 4. This step gives $\frac{12}{28}$. How do we get an equivalent for $\frac{1}{4}$ that has 28 as a denominator? We multiply by 7. This step gives $\frac{7}{28}$. Now we can add: $\frac{3}{7} + \frac{1}{4} = \frac{12}{28} + \frac{7}{28} = \frac{19}{28}$.

Models:
$$\frac{1}{3} + \frac{3}{5} = \frac{5}{15} + \frac{9}{15} = \frac{14}{15}$$
$$\frac{1}{4} + \frac{1}{8} = \frac{2}{8} + \frac{1}{8} = \frac{3}{8}$$
$$\frac{1}{8} + \frac{1}{12} = \frac{3}{24} + \frac{2}{24} = \frac{5}{24}$$

Note that for any given pair of fractions many common denominators exist. Both 4 and 7 divide evenly into 56, or 280, or 2,800. However, we always try to find the *least common denominator*. That is, we try to find the smallest number that both denominators will divide into evenly, because we prefer to work with the smallest numbers possible.

DEFINITION

The *least common denominator* is the smallest number into which the denominators will divide evenly.

When you finish an addition problem, always check the answer to see if it is reduced to lowest terms.

Find a common denominator for the following fractions. Try to find the least common denominator.

1.31 $\frac{1}{4}, \frac{3}{5}$ _____

1.32 $\frac{1}{2}, \frac{5}{6}$ _____

1.33 $\frac{3}{8}, \frac{5}{12}$ _____

1.34 $\frac{6}{7}, \frac{4}{9}$ _____

1.35 $\frac{1}{3}, \frac{3}{4}$ _____

1.36 $\frac{1}{4}, \frac{3}{10}$ _____

1.37 $\frac{6}{5}, \frac{3}{3}$ _____

1.38 $\frac{3}{8}, \frac{1}{9}$ _____

Find an equivalent to the given fraction with the new denominator.

1.39 $\frac{1}{4} = \frac{}{20}$

1.40 $\frac{1}{2} = \frac{}{6}$

1.41 $\frac{3}{8} = \frac{}{24}$

1.42 $\frac{4}{9} = \frac{}{63}$

1.43 $\frac{1}{3} = \frac{}{12}$

1.44 $\frac{1}{4} = \frac{}{20}$

1.45 $\frac{6}{5} = \frac{}{15}$

1.46 $\frac{3}{8} = \frac{}{72}$

Add the following fractions. Reduce answers to lowest terms. Show your work and circle your answer.

1.47 $\frac{1}{4} + \frac{3}{5} =$ _____

1.48 $\frac{1}{2} + \frac{5}{6} =$ _____

1.49 $\frac{3}{8} + \frac{5}{12} =$ _____

1.50 $\frac{6}{7} + \frac{4}{9} =$ _____

1.51 $\frac{1}{3} + \frac{3}{4} =$ _____

1.52 $\frac{1}{4} + \frac{3}{10} =$ _____

1.53 $\frac{6}{5} + \frac{3}{3} =$ _____

1.54 $\frac{3}{8} + \frac{1}{9} =$ _____

SUBTRACTION

Subtracting two fractions with denominators that are not the same is very similar to adding such fractions. You must first find a common denominator, then write both fractions in terms of the new denominator, and then subtract.

Model: $\frac{7}{8} - \frac{5}{12}$

Find a common denominator.
Both 8 and 12 will divide
evenly into 96, or 48, but
24 is the least common denominator. Let's use 24.

$$\frac{7}{8} - \frac{5}{12} = \frac{21}{24} - \frac{10}{24} = \frac{11}{24}$$

Subtract the following fractions. Reduce answers to lowest terms
Show your work and circle your answer.

1.55 $\frac{3}{5} - \frac{1}{4}$ = _____

1.56 $\frac{5}{6} - \frac{1}{2}$ = _____

1.57 $\frac{5}{12} - \frac{3}{8}$ = _____

1.58 $\frac{6}{7} - \frac{4}{9}$ = _____

1.59 $\frac{3}{4} - \frac{1}{3}$ = _____

1.60 $\frac{3}{10} - \frac{1}{4}$ = _____

1.61 $\frac{6}{5} - \frac{3}{3}$ = _____

1.62 $\frac{3}{8} - \frac{1}{9}$ = _____

Mixed numbers may be added in two different ways. One way is to add the whole
numbers, then add the fractions, finding
a common denominator if necessary, and
then combine the parts of the sum for the
answer.

Model: $2\frac{1}{4} + 3\frac{2}{5}$

First, add the whole numbers:
2 + 3 = 5. Then, find a common denominator for the fractions;
one common denominator is 20:
$\frac{1}{4} + \frac{2}{5} = \frac{5}{20} + \frac{8}{20}$. Next, add the
fractions: $\frac{5}{20} + \frac{8}{20} = \frac{13}{20}$. Finally,
combine the parts to the sum for
the answer: $5\frac{13}{20}$.

10

Another way to add mixed numbers is to change them to improper fractions. Then a common denominator is found (if necessary), and addition or subtraction proceeds as for any other improper fractions.

Model: $2\frac{1}{3} + 3\frac{3}{8}$

First, change $2\frac{1}{3}$ to an improper fraction with a denominator of 3: 2 is $\frac{6}{3}$ and $\frac{1}{3}$ more is $\frac{7}{3}$. Now, change $3\frac{3}{8}$ to an improper fraction with a denominator of 8: 3 is $\frac{24}{8}$ and $\frac{3}{8}$ more is $\frac{27}{8}$. Now, add $\frac{7}{3}$ and $\frac{27}{8}$. A common denominator is 24.

$$\frac{7}{3} + \frac{27}{8} = \frac{56}{24} + \frac{81}{24} = \frac{137}{24}$$

Add or subtract the following mixed numbers using the first method. Add the whole numbers; add the fractions; combine the parts of the sum for the answer. Be sure your answers are reduced to lowest terms. Show your work and circle your answer.

1.63 $2\frac{2}{3} + 4\frac{1}{8} =$ _____

1.64 $1\frac{1}{9} + 3\frac{4}{5} =$ _____

1.65 $3\frac{3}{8} + 2\frac{1}{6} =$ _____

1.66 $5\frac{5}{9} - 3\frac{1}{3} =$ _____

1.67 $2\frac{4}{5} - 1\frac{1}{2} =$ _____

1.68 $4\frac{5}{8} - 2\frac{1}{9} =$ _____

Add or subtract the following mixed numbers. First change each mixed number to an equivalent improper fraction. Then find a common denominator, and proceed as before. Be sure your answers are reduced to lowest terms. Show your work and circle your answer.

1.69 $1\frac{4}{9} + 3\frac{1}{3} =$ _____

1.70 $3\frac{1}{4} + 6\frac{1}{2} =$ _____

1.71 $\frac{1}{5} + 2\frac{1}{3} =$ _____

1.72 $3\frac{1}{6} - 1\frac{1}{2} =$ _____

1.73 $1\frac{3}{8} - \frac{3}{4} =$ _____

1.74 $4\frac{1}{2} - 2\frac{5}{8} =$ _____

MULTIPLICATION

Multiplying fractions is easier than adding or subtracting. To multiply two fractions, multiply the numerators to get the new numerator, and multiply the denominators to get the new denominator. Always be sure to check the answer to see if it can be reduced to lowest terms.

Models: $\dfrac{1}{2} \times \dfrac{3}{4} = \dfrac{1 \times 3}{2 \times 4} = \dfrac{3}{8}$

$\dfrac{6}{7} \times \dfrac{5}{12} = \dfrac{30}{84}$, which reduces to $\dfrac{5}{14}$

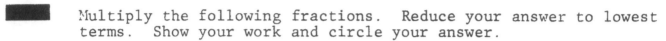 Multiply the following fractions. Reduce your answer to lowest terms. Show your work and circle your answer.

1.75 $\dfrac{3}{4} \times \dfrac{2}{3} =$ _____

1.76 $\dfrac{1}{8} \times \dfrac{1}{9} =$ _____

1.77 $\dfrac{3}{7} \times \dfrac{4}{5} =$ _____

1.78 $\dfrac{1}{2} \times \dfrac{1}{2} =$ _____

1.79 $\dfrac{5}{6} \times \dfrac{1}{2} =$ _____

1.80 $\dfrac{8}{7} \times \dfrac{3}{5} =$ _____

DIVISION

To divide one fraction into another, invert the second fraction and multiply. By *invert*, we mean to interchange the numerator and denominator; to put the numerator where the denominator was and the denominator where the numerator was.

DEFINITION

To *invert* a fraction is to write the numerator where the denominator was and the denominator where the numerator was.

Models: $\dfrac{3}{7}$ inverted is $\dfrac{7}{3}$

            $\dfrac{6}{5}$ inverted is $\dfrac{5}{6}$

After the second fraction has been inverted, multiply the fractions to divide.

Models: $\frac{7}{8} \div \frac{2}{3} = \frac{7}{8} \times \frac{3}{2} = \frac{7 \times 3}{8 \times 2} = \frac{21}{16}$

$\frac{3}{8} \div \frac{1}{2} = \frac{3}{8} \times \frac{2}{1} = \frac{3 \times 2}{8 \times 1} = \frac{6}{8} = \frac{3}{4}$

Perform the following divisions. Be sure all answers are reduced to lowest terms. Show your work and circle your answer.

1.81 $\frac{7}{12} \div \frac{3}{4} =$ _____

1.82 $\frac{5}{8} \div \frac{2}{5} =$ _____

1.83 $\frac{4}{3} \div \frac{1}{2} =$ _____

1.84 $\frac{1}{6} \div \frac{3}{5} =$ _____

1.85 $\frac{6}{7} \div \frac{3}{2} =$ _____

Multiplication and division of fractions
follow the same rules whether the fractions
are proper or improper. However, just as in
addition and subtraction, mixed numbers must
be changed to improper fractions before we
can use them in multiplication or division.

Model 1: $3\frac{1}{4} \times 1\frac{5}{8}$

$= \frac{13}{4} \times \frac{13}{8}$

$= \frac{13 \times 13}{4 \times 8} = \frac{169}{32}$

Model 2: $2\frac{1}{4} \div 1\frac{5}{6}$

$= \frac{9}{4} \div \frac{11}{6}$

$= \frac{9}{4} \times \frac{6}{11}$

$= \frac{9 \times 6}{4 \times 11} = \frac{54}{44} = \frac{27}{22}$

Also note that in the case of division by
a whole number, we write the whole number as
a fraction with a denominator of 1 before we
invert and multiply.

Model 3: $2\frac{1}{8} \div 3$

$= \frac{17}{8} \div \frac{3}{1}$

$= \frac{17}{8} \times \frac{1}{3}$

$= \frac{17 \times 1}{8 \times 3} = \frac{17}{24}$

Perform the following multiplications and divisions. Be sure answers are reduced to lowest terms. Show your work and circle your answer.

1.86 $2\frac{1}{2}$ x $1\frac{3}{8}$ = _____

1.87 $1\frac{1}{4}$ ÷ 7 = _____

1.88 $2\frac{7}{8}$ ÷ $\frac{1}{4}$ = _____

1.89 $3\frac{3}{5}$ ÷ $2\frac{1}{3}$ = _____

1.90 $6\frac{1}{2}$ ÷ $1\frac{1}{8}$ = _____

1.91 $4\frac{2}{3}$ ÷ $1\frac{5}{8}$ = _____

~~~~~ **CONSUMER APPLICATIONS** ~~~~~

Now we come to the point where we are ready to deal with real-life problems. Each of the following situations involves fractions in one way or another. See how many you can solve.

The problems have been grouped according to the operation involved in each one. You should try to analyze the problems and see why the operation we have chosen is the right one. On the tests that follow, the problems will not be grouped by operation. You will need to decide whether to use addition, subtraction, multiplication, or division.

The first set of consumer application problems requires addition. Notice how numerous fractions are in everyday situations.

Add. Show your work and circle your answer.

1.92 Joe practiced his trumpet $\frac{3}{4}$ hour on Monday and $\frac{7}{12}$ hour on Tuesday. How long did he practice altogether?

1.93 Beth needs $1\frac{2}{3}$ cups of sugar to make a cake and $2\frac{1}{4}$ cups to make a pie. How much sugar does she need to make both?

14

1.94   Good Haven Church had 12½ dozen boxes of offering envelopes.
        They ordered 14¾ dozen more. How many dozen do they have now?

1.95   You are decorating the church for the Christmas party. So far,
        you have used 12½ yards of silver rope. You have 36⅔ yards
        left. How much did you have to start with?

1.96   Barbara's club has gathered some food for needy families. Bar-
        bara distributes ⅕ of the food to one family and ⅜ to another
        family. How much of the food has she distributed?

        Fractions to be subtracted are just as
common as fractions to be added. As you
work these problems, think of times you have
used fractions to solve problems.

██████   Subtract. Show your work and circle your answer.

1.97   Jim needs 3½ yards of burlap to cover his bulletin board. His
        brother gives him 1⅛ yards. How much more does Jim need to pur-
        chase?

1.98   Susan began a trip with 18¼ gallons of gas in the gas tank of
        her car. If she used 17¾ gallons on the trip, how many gallons
        did she have left when she finished the trip?

1.99   The canister contained 6⅛ cups of flour when Mary started making
        cookies. Mary used 2½ cups. How many cups were left in the
        canister?

15

Remember that multiplying fractions is easier than adding or subtracting. These problems involve multiplication.

▬▬▬ Multiply. Show your work and circle your answer.

1.100 Find the number of bushels of wheat to be harvested from $12\frac{3}{4}$ acres if each acre yields 36 bushels.

1.101 Sarah gives each of five friends $\frac{1}{6}$ of a pie. How much of the pie does she give them altogether?

1.102 At $6\frac{1}{2}$¢ per pound of string beans, how much does 7 pounds cost?

1.103 The Owens Chemical Co. made a shipment of 450 cartons. Each carton weighed $\frac{1}{2}$ pound. What was the total weight of the shipment?

1.104 A tithe is $\frac{1}{10}$. If Mr. Henry's salary is $600 per month, what is his monthly tithe?

1.105 The Southside Band marches $1\frac{3}{4}$ miles in an hour in a parade. How far can they march in 5 hours?

1.106　The carton of milk in the refrigerator has $\frac{3}{4}$ of a quart left. John drinks $\frac{1}{2}$ of this milk. How much does he drink?

Division problems in real life often involve equal pieces or parts, distances, time periods, or other measurements. Fractions come in handy to help solve these problems.

▮　Divide. Show your work and circle your answer.

1.107　If the Southside Band can march $1\frac{1}{4}$ miles per hour, how long will it take them to parade along a 6-mile route?

1.108　A Sunday school teacher purchased 18 yards of ribbon. She cut the ribbon into several pieces, each $\frac{3}{4}$ yard long. How many pieces did she get?

1.109　Mr. James has a board that is $11\frac{1}{2}$ feet long. He wants to give an equal piece to each of 7 boys. How long will each piece be?

1.110　Mr. George owns 425 acres of land. If he divides the land into $\frac{1}{2}$-acre plots, how many plots will he have?

Review the material in this section in preparation for the Self Test. The Self Test will check your mastery of this particular section. The items missed on this Self Test will indicate specific areas where restudy is needed for mastery.

SELF TEST 1

Perform the indicated operations. Reduce answers to lowest terms. Show your work and circle your answer (each answer, 3 points).

1.01 $8\frac{1}{2} \times 3\frac{1}{2} =$ _____

1.02 $\frac{1}{16} \div \frac{3}{4} =$ _____

1.03 $\frac{8}{3} + \frac{3}{4} =$ _____

1.04 $\frac{5}{6} - \frac{1}{8} =$ _____

1.05 $6\frac{1}{4} \div 2\frac{1}{3} =$ _____

1.06 $1\frac{1}{7} \times 2\frac{1}{6} =$ _____

1.07 $14 \times \frac{7}{3} =$ _____

1.08 $\frac{9}{5} - \frac{4}{3} =$ _____

1.09 $2\frac{1}{2} + 1\frac{1}{16} =$ _____

1.010 $\frac{3}{8} \times \frac{3}{4} =$ _____

1.011 $\frac{4}{3} + \frac{1}{9} =$ _____

1.012 $\frac{1}{2} \div 7\frac{1}{3} =$ _____

1.013 $\frac{6}{10} + \frac{3}{4} =$ _____

1.014 $1\frac{3}{7} - \frac{4}{5} =$ _____

1.015 $\frac{14}{15} - \frac{1}{3} =$ _____

1.016 $\frac{9}{11} + \frac{3}{4} =$ _____

1.017 $\frac{7}{16} - \frac{3}{16} =$ _____

1.018 $6\frac{1}{2} \div 4 =$ _____

1.019 $3\frac{1}{8} - 2\frac{1}{6} =$ _____

1.020 $\frac{4}{10} \div \frac{1}{3} =$ _____

1.021 $\frac{8}{5} + \frac{7}{5} =$ _____

1.022 $\frac{6}{10} - \frac{1}{3} =$ _____

1.023 $\frac{1}{3} \div \frac{1}{4} =$ _____

1.024 $3\frac{1}{8} \times \frac{7}{16} =$ _____

1.025 $\frac{1}{3} \times \frac{11}{4} =$ _____

1.026 $\frac{7}{9} + 1\frac{1}{2} =$ _____

Solve the following problems. Reduce answers to lowest terms. Show your work and circle your answer (each answer, 4 points).

1.027   Jerry owns 640 acres of land. If he divides the land into $\frac{1}{2}$-acre plots, how many plots will he have?

1.028   A jar in the refrigerator contains $2\frac{1}{6}$ quarts of orange juice. Alice drinks $\frac{1}{6}$ of this juice. How much does she drink?

1.029   If you have $10\frac{1}{2}$ dozen rubber bands, and you order $6\frac{1}{3}$ dozen more, how many dozen do you have in all?

1.030   At $8\frac{1}{4}$¢ per pound of lima beans, how much does 5 pounds cost?

1.031   If a car averages $50\frac{1}{3}$ miles per hour, how many hours will it take to go $47\frac{1}{2}$ miles?

1.032   Susan baby-sat $3\frac{1}{4}$ hours on Friday and $2\frac{1}{2}$ hours on Saturday. How long did she baby-sit altogether?

1.033   If I start with $12\frac{1}{4}$ yards of material and use $3\frac{1}{3}$, how much do I have left?

19

1.034   How much is $\frac{3}{8}$ of $\frac{1}{4}$?

1.035   If a board that is $16\frac{3}{8}$ feet long is divided into 9 equal pieces, how long is each piece?

On the blank, write a definition for each of the following words (each answer, 3 points).

1.036   fraction _____

_____

1.037   numerator _____

_____

1.038   denominator _____

_____

1.039   proper fraction _____

_____

1.040   improper fraction _____

_____

1.041   mixed number _____

_____

1.042   equivalent fraction _____

_____

1.043   common denominator _____

_____

1.044   invert _____

_____

On the blank lines, write three items that a fraction can represent (each answer, 1 point).

1.045 a. _____

       b. _____

       c. _____

Score _____

✓ Teacher check _____

                   Initial   Date

II. DECIMALS

OBJECTIVES

6. To convert fractions to decimals.

7. To convert decimals to fractions.

8. To add, subtract, multiply, and divide numbers involving decimals.

9. To solve consumer-related problems using decimals.

The fractions that we have been talking about up to now are sometimes called common fractions. One kind of fraction is used so often and is so important that we study it separately. We call these fractions *decimal fractions*, or simply *decimals*.

~~~~~~~~~~ **TERMINOLOGY** ~~~~~~~~~~~~~~~~~~~~~~~~~~~~~

Before we define decimal fractions, let's review what we know about our number system. Remember that our number system is a place-value system. This means that the digits in a numeral have certain values depending upon their place in the numeral.

Model: In the numeral 3,473,

the 3 on the left represents 3 thousands and

the 3 on the right represents 3 ones.

We call our number system a *decimal* system, because it is based on ten and powers of ten.

DEFINITION

Decimal means based on ten, as our number system.

Now, let's learn about decimal fractions. In our place-value number system, we can represent numbers less than 1 by putting a decimal point in front of them. For example, 0.3 means $\frac{3}{10}$, and 0.14 means $\frac{14}{100}$.

A decimal fraction is a special fraction, one whose denominator is always ten or a power of ten. It is written with a decimal point to its left, to identify it as being less than 1. We also write a zero to the left of the decimal point to make certain we recognize the number as a decimal. Each place to the right of the decimal point has a certain value, just as each place to the left has a special value.

DEFINITION

A *decimal fraction* is a number less than 1, **represented in place-**value notation using a decimal point.

Mixed numbers are very easy to write using decimal fractions. Simply separate the whole number part from the fraction part with a decimal point.

Model 1:   Write $147\frac{37}{100}$ as 147.37.

How do decimal fractions relate to common fractions? We have already seen that if the denominator of a common fraction is ten or a power of ten, we can simply write it as a decimal fraction, using place-value notation. What about other common fractions? How can we make decimal fractions out of them? To make a decimal fraction out of a common fraction, divide the numerator by the denominator. (A calculator is very useful for this procedure.)

Model 2:   To convert $\frac{1}{4}$ to a decimal fraction, divide 4 into 1. Note that we can write a decimal point to the right of a whole number and add as many zeros as we like, without changing the value of the number. As a matter of fact, we can add zeros to the right of any decimal fraction without changing its value. Also note that we align the decimal point in the quotient of our division problems above the decimal point of the dividend. (If you use a calculator, it will take care of lining up the decimal points for you.)

```
        0.25
    4)1.00
        8
       20
       20
```

So we see that $\frac{1}{4}$ is equivalent to 0.25 as a decimal fraction.

Not all common fractions turn out even when you convert them to decimal fractions. Some common fractions are repeating decimals.

Model 3: $\frac{1}{3}$ =
```
    0.3333333
 3)1.0000000
```

This division could go on forever and always keep on producing 3's. We can indicate this result by a bar over the 3 (like this: $\frac{1}{3}$ = 0.$\overline{3}$) or we can simply round a repeating decimal to as many places as we like.

Some common fractions would come out even if we carried the division out to several places, but we may not want to carry it out that far. In such cases we round to as many places as we choose or are instructed.

Model 4: $\frac{6}{17}$ = 0.353 or 0.35 or 0.3529 or 0.35294

Convert the following common fractions to decimals. If the decimals are repeating, place a bar over the repeating digits. Otherwise, round to three decimal places. You may use a calculator if you have one or can easily borrow one.

2.1 $\frac{1}{2}$ = _____

2.2 $\frac{1}{3}$ = _____

2.3 $\frac{3}{4}$ = _____

2.4 $\frac{3}{5}$ = _____

2.5 $\frac{5}{6}$ = _____

2.6 $\frac{1}{7}$ = _____

2.7 $\frac{7}{8}$ = _____

2.8 $\frac{4}{9}$ = _____

2.9 $\frac{6}{10}$ = _____

2.10 $\frac{3}{20}$ = _____

CONSUMER MATHEMATICS
2

LIFEPAC TEST

<table>
<tr><td>69
86</td><td>Name _____
Date _____
Score _____</td></tr>
</table>

CONSUMER MATHEMATICS 2: LIFEPAC TEST

Perform the indicated operations. Reduce fractions to lowest terms;
round decimals to 3 places. Show your work and circle your answer
(Each answer, 3 points).

1. $8\frac{1}{2} \times 3\frac{1}{2} =$ _____

2. $47.3 \div 0.017 =$ _____

3. $42.3 - 1.094 =$ _____

4. $\frac{1}{6} \div \frac{3}{8} =$ _____

5. $1.6 \times 0.0318 =$ _____

6. $\frac{5}{6} - \frac{3}{8} =$ _____

7. $\frac{4}{13} + \frac{5}{39} =$ _____

8. $4.1 + 0.032 + 147 =$ _____

Complete the following chart (each answer, 3 points).

	Base	Rate	Percentage
9.	_____	14%	38
10.	463	91%	_____
11.	1,042	_____	516
12.	_____	65%	14
13.	43	25%	_____
14.	140	_____	97

Solve the following problems. Show your work and circle your answer
(each answer, 4 points).

15. Jerry owns 640 acres of land. If he divides the land into
$\frac{1}{2}$-acre plots, how many plots will he have?

16. If you have $14\frac{1}{2}$ dozen boxes of envelopes, and you order $3\frac{1}{4}$
dozen more, how many dozen boxes will you have in all?

2

17. If a board that is 4⅛ feet long is divided into 7 equal how long will each piece be?

18. If I start with 3⅛ yards of material and use 1½ yards, how many yards do I have left?

19. How much does Martha earn by babysitting for 4.5 hours at $2.25 per hour?

20. If 843 units cost $1,268.50 to produce, what is the cost of each unit, to the nearest cent?

21. If 70 kilometers is equal to 231,000 feet, how many feet are in 70 meters?

22. Of the 640 people present at the rally, 400 were female. What per cent were female?

23. Peter earns $11,250 per year. He spends 38% of this income on food. How much does he spend on food?

24. Add 3.112, 475.3, and 37.

25.   How much is a tax of 5% on a purchase of $27.50?

NOTES

Sometimes we may want to change a decimal fraction to a common fraction. The calculator doesn't help us. We must make the change by hand or mentally.

The process has two main steps. First, write the decimal fraction as a common fraction, using as the denominator the proper power of ten. Second, reduce to lowest terms. To find the proper power of ten, count the digits to the right of the decimal point and use that many zeros after the 1.

Models: $0.37 = \frac{37}{100}$ (2 digits; 2 zeros)

$0.037 = \frac{37}{1,000}$ (3 digits; 3 zeros)

$0.3 = \frac{3}{10}$ (1 digit; 1 zero)

$3.7 = 3\frac{7}{10}$ (whole number to left of decimal point; one digit to right)

The following models show the steps in changing decimals to common fractions.

Models: $0.25 = \frac{25}{100} = \frac{1}{4}$

$0.165 = \frac{165}{1,000} = \frac{33}{200}$

$0.375 = \frac{375}{1,000} = \frac{75}{200} = \frac{15}{40} = \frac{3}{8}$

Convert the following decimal fractions to common fractions. Reduce to lowest terms.

2.11   0.2 = _____

2.12   0.625 = _____

2.13   0.75 = _____

2.14   0.5 = _____

2.15   0.03 = _____

~~~~~~~~~~~~~ SKILLS ~~~~~~~~~~~~~

Adding and subtracting decimal fractions and mixed numbers containing decimal points is a cinch! All you need to do is line up the decimal points, and then add or subtract using basic addition and subtraction facts.

Model 1:   To add 3.147 and 142.1, line up
           the decimal points.

```
      3.147
  + 142.1
    145.247
```

Model 2:   To subtract 0.51 from 47.3,
           line up the decimal points.
           Add a zero to the right of the
           three to make it easier to sub-
           tract.

```
    47.30
  -  0.51
    46.79
```

When you use a calculator to add and subtract decimals, the calculator automatically
lines up the decimal point for you.

██████   Add or subtract the following numbers. Even if you use a calculator to get the answer, rewrite the problem with the decimal
points aligned.

2.16   3.14 + 17.8 = _____   2.19   5,387.1 - 16.5 = _____

2.17   7.61 − 0.043 = _____   2.20   107.3 + 0.8598 = _____

2.18   142.3 + 0.07 = _____   2.21   3.1 − 0.674   = _____

When you multiply decimals by hand, the
rule you need to remember is this: the
product has as many decimal places as are in
both numbers that are multiplied.

Model: 1.14
        x 0.3
        0.342

           Since the top number has two deci-
           mal places and the bottom number
           has one decimal place, the answer
           must have three decimal places.

Multiply the following numbers (you may use a calculator).

2.22   3.7 x 0.14 = _____   2.24   14.3 x 0.017 = _____

2.23   14.8 x 1.7 = _____   2.25   3.9 x 0.6421 = _____

One type of multiplication is very easy when we use decimals: multiplication by ten or any power of ten. To multiply by ten or a power of ten, move the decimal point to the right as many places as are zeros in the power of ten.

    Models: 6.421 x 10 = 64.21 (decimal point moved right one place)

                6.421 x 1000 = 6,421 (decimal point moved right three places)

                6.421 x 100000 = 642,100 (decimal point moved right five places; zeros added as necessary to make enough places)

 Perform the following multiplications.

2.26   3 x 1,000 = _____   2.29   73.4142 x 1,000 = _____

2.27   4.7314 x 10 = _____   2.30   99 x 100,000 = _____

2,28   167.4 x 100 = _____

Division by ten or a power of ten is just as easy as multiplication. Simply move the decimal point to the *left* as many places as are zeros in the power of ten. (Again, add zeros as necessary.)

Models: 14 ÷ 10 = 1.4 (one zero; move left one place)

14 ÷ 100 = 0.14 (two zeros; move left two places)

14 ÷ 1000 = 0.014 (three zeros; move left three places; add a zero to make enough places)

▆▆▆▆ Perform the following divisions.

2.31   1.47 ÷ 10 = _____   2.33   5.734 ÷ 1,000 =_____

2.32   498.3 ÷ 100 =_____   2.34   0.04 ÷ 10 =   _____

To divide numbers involving decimal points, we need to remember this procedure: always divide by a whole number. Therefore, when we are given a division problem involving decimals, we first multiply both divisor and dividend by the proper power of ten to make the divisor a whole number. Then we proceed with the division. The decimal point in the quotient goes directly above the decimal point in the dividend. Let's see how it works.

Model: Divide 0.374 by 1.12
         Multiply both divisor (1.12)
         and dividend (0.374) by 100
         to make the divisor a whole
         number. Remember, to multiply
         by 100, move the decimal point
         to the right 2 places. Now
         we have 37.4 ÷ 112.

```
        0.3339   or 0.334, rounded to
112)37.4000          3 decimal
    33 6            places
     3 80
     3 36
      440
      336
     1040
     1008
       32
```

28

Note that we keep adding zeros
until we have the division carried out as far as we want it.

Perform the following divisions. Show the multiplication you
would do to make the divisor a whole number. Round the answer
to three decimal places. (You may use a calculator.)

Model: $17.3 \div 0.13 = 1{,}730 \div 13 = 133.077$

2.35 $1.31 \div 0.47 =$ _____

2.36 $147.4 \div 1.8 =$ _____

2.37 $0.64 \div 3.8 =$ _____

2.38 $14 \div 4.11 =$ _____

~~~~~~ **CONSUMER APPLICATIONS** ~~~~~~~~~~~~~~~~~~~~~~~~

The following problems use decimals in
one form or another. One common use of decimals is money problems. When we write dollars
and cents, we are really writing a decimal.
The decimal point in a dollars-and-cents amount
separates the dollars from the cents. It
tells us how many whole dollars we have (to
the left of the decimal point) and how many
hundredths of a dollar we have (to the right
of the decimal point): one cent is one hund-
redth of a dollar.
    Another increasingly common use of deci-
mals is in the system of measure called the
metric system. This system is a decimal system.
The following chart shows how the measurements
in the system relate to one another.

1 kilometer = 1,000 meters   1 kilogram = 1,000 grams

1 hectometer = 100 meters   1 hectogram = 100 grams

1 decameter = 10 meters   1 decagram = 10 grams

1 meter   = 1 meter   1 gram   = 1 gram

1 decimeter = $\frac{1}{10}$ of a meter   1 decigram = $\frac{1}{10}$ of a gram

1 centimeter = $\frac{1}{100}$ of a meter   1 centigram = $\frac{1}{100}$ of a gram

1 millimeter = $\frac{1}{1,000}$ of a meter   1 milligram = $\frac{1}{1,000}$ of a gram

29

Model: If 35 meters is equal to 115.5
            feet, how many feet are in 35
            kilometers?

            Solution: Since 1 kilometer =
            1,000 meters, multiply by 1,000;
            35 kilometers = 35,000 meters =
            115,500 feet.

████   Solve the following problems. You may use a calculator. If you
        do not have or cannot use a calculator, show your work and circle
        your answer.

2.39   If 1 kilogram = 2.206 pounds, how many pounds are in a gram?

2.40   Add 2,034; 571.835; and 0.082.

2.41   Company Q has 67 cartons valued at $2.85 each. What is their
        total worth?

2.42   A firm produces 16,200 units at a total cost of $37,585.60.
        Find the cost per unit to the nearest cent.

2.43   In October, Glen Haven Church had receipts of $3,424.72 and
        expenditures of $2,147.31. Calculate the balance for the month.

2.44   Find the area of a floor that measures 12.75 ft. by 10.5 ft.

2.45   A super train travels 1,500 miles in 12.5 hours. How many miles
        does it travel in one hour?

2.46   Before polishing, a steel plate was 2.342 inches thick. After
         polishing, it was 2.087 inches thick. How much was removed in
         polishing?

2.47   How much would you pay for an item if you paid $84.70 per month
         for 36 months?

2.48   Lynn can complete 3.5 long divisions in 1 hour. How many can
         he finish in 7.5 hours?

2.49   Jack drove at an average speed of 47.3 miles per hour for 2.5
         hours. How far did he drive?

2.50   If a sheet of steel is 0.002 of an inch thick, find the height
         of 10,250 sheets stacked together.

2.51   Hank Speedwell drove 1,120 miles in 12.5 hours. What was his
         average speed in miles per hour?

2.52   Calculate the tithe of an income of $12,347 by dividing by 10.

2.53   If a case of 24 cans of peaches costs $7.50, how much does each
         can cost, to the nearest cent?

Review the material in this section in preparation for the Self Test. This Self Test will
check your mastery of this particular section as well as your knowledge of the previous
section.

SELF TEST 2

On the blanks identify the fractions as proper, improper, or mixed. If
the fraction is equivalent to 1, write 1 in the blank (each answer, 2
points).

2.01 $\frac{7}{3}$ _____   2.02 $3\frac{1}{2}$ _____

2.03 $\frac{147}{147}$ _____   2.04 $\frac{4}{5}$ _____

2.05 $\frac{6}{5}$ _____   2.06 $4\frac{1}{3}$ _____

Perform the indicated operations. Reduce fractions to lowest
terms; round decimals to three decimal places. Show your work
and circle your answer (each answer, 3 points).

2.07 $\frac{1}{3} + \frac{3}{4} =$ _____

2.08 $4.131 \div 16 =$ _____

2.09 $\frac{16}{5} \times \frac{1}{9} =$ _____

2.010 $43.7 + 0.042 + 68 =$ _____

2.011 $\frac{1}{16} \div \frac{3}{4} =$ _____

2.012 $\frac{3}{4} - \frac{1}{4} =$ _____

2.013 $143.6 - 0.414 =$ _____

2.014 $6\frac{1}{2} + 1\frac{1}{7} =$ _____

2.015 $3.4721 \times 100 =$ _____

2.016 $47.3 \times 0.012 =$ _____

2.017 $48.2 \div 1.43 =$ _____

Define the following words (each answer, 3 points).

2.018   common denominator   _____

_____

2.019   proper fraction   _____

_____

2.020   decimal   _____

_____

2.021   reduced to lowest terms   _____

_____

2.022   decimal fraction   _____

_____

Solve the following problems. Show your work and circle your answer (each answer, 4 points).

2.023   If a sheet of aluminum is 0.04 inches thick, find the height of 76,421 sheets stacked together.

2.024   How much is $\frac{1}{9}$ of $\frac{3}{8}$?

2.025   At 4.7¢ per pound of rice, how much does 10.5 pounds cost?

2.026   If 843 units cost $16,421.40 to produce, how much does each unit cost to produce, to the nearest cent?

2.027   If 70 meters is equal to 231 feet, how many feet are in 70 kilometers?

2.028   A plane travels 6,424 miles in $11\frac{1}{8}$ hours. What is its average speed in miles per hour? (Hint: Change $11\frac{1}{8}$ to a decimal.)

2.029   Find the volume of a rectangular solid with edges of 4.6, 3.19, and 2.7 units. (Hint: volume = length x width x height)

2.030   What is the total cost of an item if you pay $13.50 per month for 24 months?

2.031   Mrs. Jones cuts a ribbon that is $7\frac{1}{4}$ yards long into 11 pieces. How long is each piece?

2.032   What does Susan earn by babysitting for 3.5 hours at $1.75 per hour?

III. PERCENT

You can hardly read the newspaper these days without encountering the symbol %. "Crime rises 37%." "Ivory Soap -- 99 $\frac{44}{100}$% pure." "53% of the doctors surveyed chewed gum."

This symbol, %, is read *percent*. It means *per hundred*, or *out of every hundred*, or *hundredths*.

DEFINITION

Percent means per hundred, out of every hundred, or hundredths.

For example, the statement, "61% of the voters approved the measure" means "61 voters per hundred approved," or " 61 voters out of every hundred approved," or "61 hundredths of the voters approved." Let's learn how to work with this concept.

To be able to use percents, we need to be able to convert them to decimals. Conversion of percents to decimals is easy to do. Just drop the % sign and move the decimal point two places to the left.

Model: 37% = 0.37

This method is logical, since one meaning of % is hundredths, and 0.37 is 37 hundredths. I like to remember this trick by thinking of the two little zeros on the % sign as decimal places. When we take the % sign away, we have to get the two decimal places back by moving the decimal point to the left.

▬▬▬ Change these percents to decimals.

3.1   67% = _____   3.4   0.4% = _____

3.2   3% = _____   3.5   138.4% = _____

3.3   147% = _____   3.6   14% = _____

Of course, changing from a decimal to a percent is simply the same procedure in reverse. Move the decimal point two places to the right and add the % sign.

Model: 0.473 = 47.3%

▬▬▬ Change these decimals to percents.

3.7   0.43 = _____   3.10   0.7 = _____

3.8   1.3 = _____   3.11   0.65 = _____

3.9   0.01 = _____   3.12   0.04 = _____

Often we are concerned with a certain percent of something. The word *cf* usually means to multiply. We change the % to a decimal before we multiply.

Model: 37% of 350 = 0.37 x 350 = 129.5

▬▬▬ Find the following quantities.

3.13   6% of 124 = _____

3.14   103% of 19 = _____

3.15   42.1% of 375.4 = _____

3.16   5.4% of 900 =   _____

3.17   13% of 130 =   _____

3.18   75.5% of 299.8 = _____

~~~~~~~~~ FRACTIONS ~~~~~~~~~~~~~~~~~~~~~~~~~~~~~~~~~~

Occasionally, we want to change a percent to a common fraction. The easiest way is to change the percent to a decimal, and then change the decimal to a common fraction. (Remember how to make the change?

Model: $25\% = 0.25 = \frac{25}{100} = \frac{1}{4}$

If not, perhaps you should review the previous section.)

■■■■ Convert the following percents to decimals and then to common fractions.

3.19   80% = _____   3.22   45% = _____

3.20   75% = _____   3.23   2% = _____

3.21   87.5% = _____   3.24   12.5% = _____

The process of converting a fraction to a percent is just the reverse, as you might suspect. First change the fraction to a decimal (remember?) and then convert the decimal to a percent.

Model: $\frac{1}{7} = 0.1429 = 14.29\%$

■■■■ Convert the following fractions to decimals and then to percents. Round the decimals to three places before converting to percents.

3.25 $\frac{1}{3}$ = _____   3.28 $\frac{3}{5}$ = _____

3.26 $\frac{9}{10}$ = _____   3.29 $\frac{1}{2}$ = _____

3.27 $\frac{1}{8}$ = _____   3.30 $\frac{1}{7}$ = _____

~~~~~~~ CONSUMER APPLICATIONS ~~~~~~~~~~~~~~~~~~~~~~~~

One of the most frequent uses of percents in the real world is in problems called base-rate-percentage problems.

Model: 50%   of   120   is   60.
           (rate)   (base)   (percentage)

Note several things about the
statement:

1. The rate always has the %
    sign.

2. The word *of* points to the
    base.

3. The other figure, the one
    without the % or the *of*,
    is the percentage.

In every base-rate-percentage problem,
we will be given two of the three figures
and asked to find the third. Let's look
at all three, one at a time, and see what
to do if we are asked to find it.

THE PERCENTAGE

Suppose the problem says, "How much is
47% of 130?" Note that we have the rate (47%;
the % sign identifies it) and the base (130;
the word *of* identifies the base). The
missing item is the percentage. Follow
this rule to find the percentage.

RULE

To find the percentage, multiply the base by the rate.

Note that you will need to change the
rate from a percent to a decimal before
you multiply.

Model: How much is 47% of 130?
            130 x 0.47 = 61.1

█████   Find the percentage in the following problems.

3.31   24% of 1,321 is how much? _____

3.32   What is 75% of 90?   _____

3.33   How much is 19.5% of 600? _____

3.34   What is 48% of 576?   _____

3.35   If you take 12% of 750, what do you get? _____

3.36   How much is 8% of 1,249?   _____

THE RATE

     Suppose the problem says, "What per
cent of 124 is 16?" Note that we do not
have the rate. We have the base (124;--
note the *of*) and the percentage (16).
Follow this rule to find the rate.

```
RULE

To find the rate, divide the percentage by the base.
```

     Your answer will be a decimal, so you
will need to change it to a percent.

     Model: What percent of 124 is 16?
               16 : 124 = 0.129 = 12.9%

■■■■   Find the rate in the following problems (round to three decimal
        places before changing to percent).

3.37   What percent of 371 is 120?   _____

3.38   One hundred fifty is what percent of 200? _____

3.39   Eighty-four is what percent of 212?   _____

3.40   What percent of 85 is 10?   _____

3.41   What percent of 142 is 317?   _____

3.42   Fifteen is what percent of 1,500?   _____

THE BASE

Suppose the problem says, "12% of what number is 64?" Now we are missing the base. (The problem says *of what number.*) Follow this rule to find the base.

RULE

To find the base, divide the percentage by the rate.

Be sure to change the rate from a per cent to a decimal before you divide.

Model: 12% of what number is 64?
            $64 \div 0.12 = 533.\overline{3}$

███   Find the base in the following problems.

3.43   10% of _____ is 81.

3.44   100 is 19% of what number?   _____

3.45   303 is 93% of what?   _____

3.46   12.5% of _____ is 130.

3.47   62 is 112% of what number?   _____

3.48   50 is 85% of what? _____

Now here are all three rules in a nut-shell.

BASE-RATE-PERCENTAGE RULES
If you do not have the percentage, multiply.

If you do have the percentage, divide it by the other number you have.

██████   Find the missing element in the following base-rate-percentage problems.

3.49   12% of what number is 42?   _____

3.50   What percent of 621 is 300? _____

3.51   43 is 120% of what number?   _____

3.52   16.5% of 4,371 is how much? _____

3.53   How much is 81% of 403?   _____

3.54   18% of _____ is 99.

Use all the concepts of this section to solve the following problems. Show your work in the space provided, and circle your answer.

3.55   Seventy-two people are enrolled in the Bible Learners department. If 37.5% are absent, how many people are absent?

3.56   Phil planted 3 bushels of corn. His harvest was 349% of what he planted. How much did he harvest?

3.57   Of the 640 people present at the rally, 400 were female. What per cent were female?

3.58   Last year's sales were $200,000. Sales have increased by 250% this year. How much is the increase?

3.59   If last year's sales were $200,000 and this year's increase was 250%, how much are this year's sales?

3.60   Peter earns $11,250 per year, of which 31% is spent on food. What amount is spent yearly on food?

3.61   Martha spends $227.50 per week. This amount is 91% of what she earns. How much does she earn per week?

3.62   Bill earns $87.50 per week; Jack earns $70.00 per week. What per cent of Bill's salary is Jack's?

REVIEW Before you take this last Self Test, you may want to do one or more of these self checks.

1. _____ Read the objectives. Determine if you can do them.
2. _____ Restudy the material related to any objectives that you cannot do.
3. _____ Use the SQ3R study procedure to review the material:
   a. **S**can the sections.
   b. **Q**uestion yourself again (review the questions you wrote initially).
   c. **R**ead to answer your questions.
   d. **R**ecite the answers to yourself.
   e. **R**eview areas you didn't understand.
4. _____ Review all activities and Self Tests, writing a correct answer for each wrong answer.

SELF TEST 3

Define the following words (each answer, 3 points).

3.01   fraction _____

_____

3.02   decimal fraction _____

_____

3.03   numerator _____

_____

3.04   denominator _____

_____

3.05   mixed number _____

_____

3.06   percent _____

_____

3.07   improper fraction _____

_____

Write the correct answers on the blanks in the following chart. Round decimals to 3 places (each answer, 3 points).

	Percent	Decimal Fraction	Common Fraction
3.08	a. _____	b. _____	$\frac{1}{4}$
3.09	a. _____	b. _____	$\frac{4}{9}$
3.010	45%	a. _____	b. _____
3.011	a. _____	1.4	b. _____
3.012	a. _____	0.625	b. _____
3.013	50%	a. _____	b. _____

Solve the following problems. Show your work and circle your answer (each answer, 4 points).

3.014 George studied $\frac{3}{4}$ hour on Monday and $\frac{7}{8}$ hour on Tuesday. How long did he study altogether on both days?

3.015 Of the 103 people enrolled in mathematics class, 91% are present. How many are present?

3.016 If 3 kilograms = 6.618 pounds, how many pounds are in 3 grams?

3.017 Last year's sales were $14,200. Sales have increased 57% this year. How much is the increase?

3.018 Sandra needs $4\frac{1}{2}$ cups of flour for one kind of cookie and $3\frac{1}{2}$ cups for another kind. How much would she need for both kinds?

3.019   Mr. Farmer plans on a 315% harvest.   How many bushels of corn
        must he sow to reap 1,000 bushels?

3.020   Mr. Grocer has 421 dozen eggs valued at $0.59 per dozen.   How
        much are the eggs worth altogether?

3.021   What is a tithe of an income of $91.50?

3.022   If the total attendance is 424, and my class has 79 present, what
        percent of the total attendance is the attendance in my class?

3.023   Mrs. Lapp gives each of 4 children $\frac{1}{8}$ of a cake.   How much of the
        cake does she give them in all?

3.024   On Team B 84% of the football players weigh more than 200 pounds.
        If 37 men are on the team, how many weigh more than 200 pounds?

Write the correct answers on the blanks in the following chart (each
answer, 3 points).

	Base	Rate	Percentage
3.025	$642	14%	_____
3.026	_____	29%	403
3.027	1043	_____	14
3.028	14	83%	_____

45

3.029   63   _____   51

3.030   _____   58%   296

```
 96 /
    / 119
```

Score _____

Teacher check _____
　　　　　　　　Initial　　　Date

GLOSSARY

common denominator. Of two fractions, a number into which both denominators will divide evenly.

common factor. Of a fraction, a number that divides evenly into both numerator and denominator.

decimal. Based on ten.

decimal fraction. A number with a value less than 1, written in place-value notation, using a decimal point.

denominator. Of a fraction, the number below the horizontal bar.

equivalent fractions. Fractions that have the same numerical value.

fraction. A symbol consisting of three parts: a horizontal bar, a whole number above the bar, and a whole number below the bar.

improper fraction. A fraction with a numerator greater than its denominator, giving it a value greater than 1.

invert. Of fractions, to put the numerator below the bar and the denominator above the bar.

least common denominator. Of two fractions, the smallest number into which both denominators will divide evenly.

mixed number. A number with a whole number part and a fraction part.

numerator. Of a fraction, the number above the horizontal bar.

percent. Per hundred; out of every hundred; hundredths.

proper fraction. A fraction with a value less than 1.

reduced to lowest terms. Of fractions, such that the only common factor of both numerator and denominator is 1.

REVIEW   Before taking the LIFEPAC Test, you may want to do one or more of these self checks.
1. _____ Read the objectives. Check to see if you can do them.
2. _____ Restudy the material related to any objective that you cannot do.
3. _____ Use the SQ3R study procedure to review the material.
4. _____ Review activities, Self Tests, and LIFEPAC Glossary.
5. _____ Restudy areas of weakness indicated by the last Self Test.

47